JAK cartoons

BOOK NINETEEN

from

THE LONDON EVENING
STANDARD

and

The Mail ON SUNDAY

Published by Associated Magazines Ltd., for
Mail Newspapers p.l.c., London

ISBN 0 85144 420 2

Printed in Great Britain by
Spottiswoode Ballantyne Ltd., Colchester and London.

September 29, 1986

A look into the future . . .

"... First we gave up nuclear energy ...!"

October 9, 1986

Jaguar launched a new range of models.

"There go the Joneses, showing off their new Jag!"

October 10, 1986

Haringey Council ruled that Baa Baa Black Sheep should become Baa Baa Green Sheep.

The Queen and Prince Philip on a State visit to China.

"If you don't like it, I'll get something else sent in from a different take-away!"

October 14, 1986

Drugs were found in bottles of champagne at Heathrow.

"Personally, I find this London Airport champagne rather too dry!"

October 15, 1986

The Reykjavik talks between Reagan and Gorbachev didn't go too well.

"What do you mean, Mikhail, IF we go to Washington?"

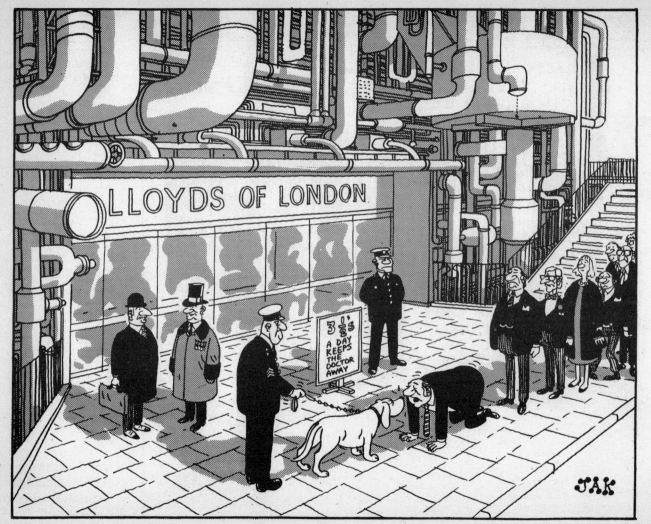

October 16, 1986

A report said that three half-pints a day were enough for any man.

"We're trying to cut down on heavy drinking at lunch-time!"

October 17, 1986

An entrepreneur bought a public lavatory and considered turning it into a restaurant.

"I can assure you, sir, everything has been personally passed by the manager!"

October 20, 1986

"You've got a hell of a lot of catching up to do, Wilkins – now, this is a ONE, this is a TWO!"

October 22, 1986

The Big Bang was about to revolutionise the Stock Exchange.

"Come Monday, pater, just by touching one weeny little button I could wipe-out the family's entire share holdings!"

October 24, 1986

After tit-for-tat expulsions of American and Russian diplomats, Moscow stopped Americans employing local people in their embassy as domestic staff.

"See the Ambassador? I am the Ambassador!"

October 27, 1986

An overloaded brand-new computer went out of action for a time on the City's big day.

"Hold it everybody! – the main frame computer's working again!"

October 28, 1986

Jeffrey Archer resigned as deputy chairman of the Tory Party after giving £2,000 to a prostitute to leave the country. He denied ever meeting the woman.

"I've changed my mind, but what a pity with so many wonderful names to choose from!"

October 30, 1986

Essex Police were criticised for their handling of a murder case.

"That's a bit of luck, Fingers – it's the Essex Police!"

October 31, 1986

Sheik Yamani was relieved of his job as Saudi oil minister, which he had held since 1962.

"That's not Sheik Yamani resigning, is it?"

November 4, 1986

Some British nurses and other medical staff were arrested and deported from Saudi Arabia because the house they were in had equipment for making alcoholic drinks.

"Have a glass of this, Mustapha, it will help to relax you!"

Allegations were made in some quarters about Princess Michael of Kent's family background.

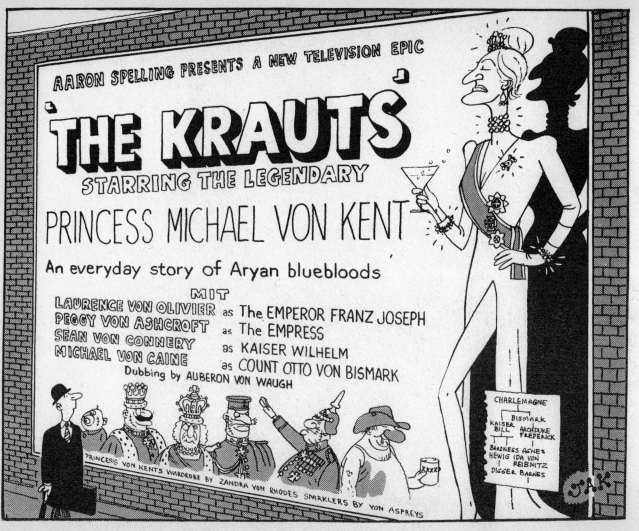

November 6, 1986

Market Research celebrated its 40th birthday with a wealth of nostalgia.

"Personally, Doris, I preferred you in those whalebone corsets you used to wear!"

JAK

November 18, 1986

Sir Robert Armstrong, Cabinet Secretary, gave evidence in the Australian court where the Government was trying to stop publication of Peter Wright's memoirs about his MI5 career.

"Thank you, Sir Robert – next witness!"

November 19, 1986

The Government planned more and franker advertising about AIDS.

"This AIDS thing must be a lot more serious than we thought, bishop!"

November 20, 1986

The don't drink-and-drive campaign is always open to new ideas . . .

"This is a gadget that tells us if you were thinking of having a drink!"

November 21, 1986

The USSR lifted its ban on free enterprise shops.

"Look out! Here come the shoplifters!"

November 24, 1986

A group of Hell's Angels managed to get a mortgage and buy a house in Windsor, to the dismay of local residents.

"**Apparently, they're not waiting for their deposit back.**"

November 28, 1986

The Australian judge in the Spycatcher case was not averse to frank comments in court.

". . . and provided it's not banned by the British Government, MY book about this farcical cock-up will be published next year!"

December 1, 1986

In Australia, Peter Wright said he was approached by Lord Rothschild (with Government approval, the ex-MI5 man thought) to help Chapman Pincher with a book about the Intelligence Service.

"Follow him and check if he's living beyond his means!"

December 2, 1986

Some people complained about explicit sex scenes in Dennis Potter's "The Singing Detective" series on TV.

"Personally, I like it – but we'll have to see what the Commissioner thinks!"

Guinness, long famed for its "good for you" ads, was being investigated by the Department of Trade about the takeover of Distillers.

December 4, 1986

Neil Kinnock, on a visit to the United States, was not proving a major attraction.

"I said, it's stopped raining outside, Maw!"

December 5, 1986

The Spycatcher case had revealed weaknesses in MI5.

"I want a dedicated, ruthless body to take over MI5!"

December 9, 1986

After nearly a year the Swedish police had no idea who killed the Prime Minister, Olof Palme.

"The bad news is, we're being investigated by the police – the good news is – they're Swedish!"

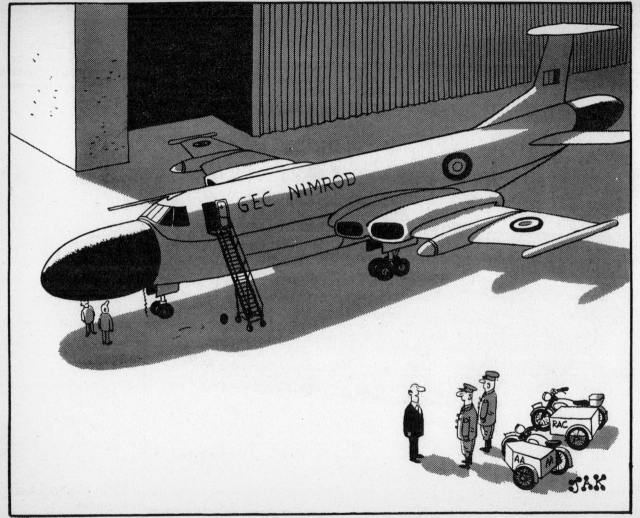

December 11, 1986

Which early warning system – British (GEC Nimrod) or American (Boeing AWACS)? The latter was chosen, eventually.

"It was all right until it went for its first service!"

December 12, 1986

Neil Kinnock launched the
Labour Party policy to ban
nuclear weapons from Britain
and spend more on conventional
forces.

JAK

**Field Marshal Von
Kinnock**

December 15, 1986

Sir John Sainsbury, chairman of the supermarket chain, is to become chairman of the Royal Opera House.

"I'm looking for the food hall!"

December 16, 1986

James Anderton, Manchester's Chief Constable, said in a controversial speech that AIDS was a punishment for immoral behaviour.

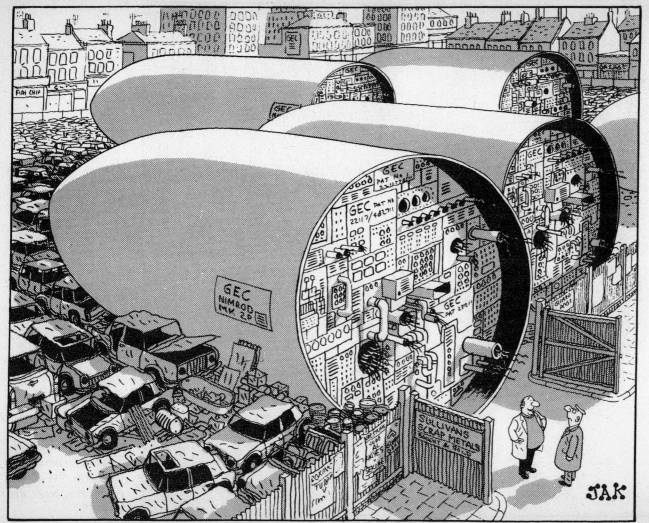

December 19, 1986

Boeing's AWACS early warning radar system had been chosen in preference to the British (GEC) Nimrod . . .

"You could use them for all sorts of things!"

December 23, 1986

James Anderton's pronouncements from on high continued to make news.

"Two messages for the Chief Constable . . . one from the Police Authority and one from God!"

December 29, 1986

The annual ritual – the after-Christmas sales . . .

"I give up – what did you girls get this year at the Selfridges Sale!"

January 2, 1987

A word new to many people, used to describe shady dealers in the stock market, hit the headlines.

"It's the Insider Dealers' Marching Band!"

That Spycatcher case wouldn't go away . . .

"I must say, Rothschild, for a man who shuns publicity, you haven't done half bad this week!"

Under the 30-year ru[l]
Cabinet papers were
released, shedding ne[w]
light on Britain's
disastrous Suez invas[ion]
of 1956.

"If it wasn't for these Suez papers, no-one would ever have discovered the truth about
Parker-Bowles and the regimental mascot!"

January 5, 1987

The United States threatened to slap a 200 per cent duty on some European imports, including gin, because they reckoned they were losing out on Spanish markets since Spain joined the EEC.

"We'd like you guys to know we're gonna keep on drinking your gin!"

January 8, 1987

Prince Edward, not enjoying the Royal Marines officer training course, was wondering whether to stay on . . .

"The next time you call a recruit 'a mummy's boy', find out who his mummy is!"

January 11, 1987

The Prince had made up his mind to bid the Marines farewell.

"Apart from four months with the Royal Marines, do you have any other experience?"

January 12, 1987

Of course, Prince Edward had to explain why he preferred Civvy Street . . .

". . . drinking, swearing and fighting with broken botles and razors every night – and those were the officers!

January 9, 1987

This regiment had been on duty in Kenya and were offered free AIDS tests in case they had caught the virus.

January 14, 1987

Britain was in the grip of its coldest weather for years.

"You should get a gold medal for that in this weather, young man!"

January 16, 1987

Scandal was rife in the City . . .

"Do you get the feeling that 'something in the City' now means 24-hour police surveillance?"

February 13, 1987

Mrs Cynthia Payne was found not guilty on charges of controlling prostitutes.

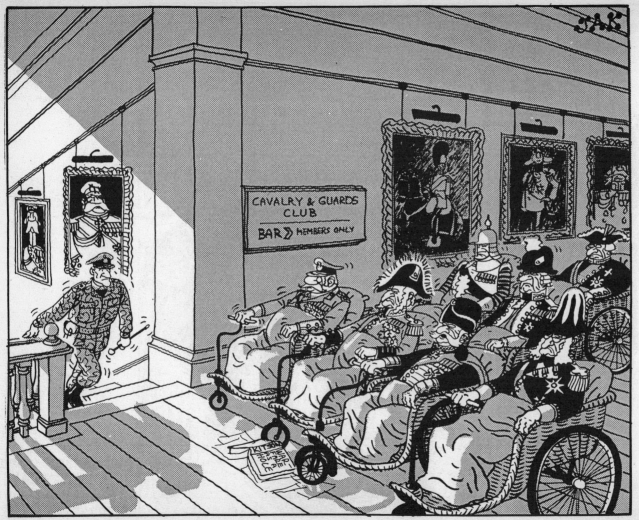

February 17, 1987

General Sir Frank Kitson (aged 60) declared that military chiefs were too old and not capable of taking decisions.

"Ah, Kitson! The committee would like a word with you!"

February 19, 1987

Tamils, claiming to be refugees, stripped to their underpants at Heathrow when officials tried to get them on a plane back to Bangladesh, where they had come from.

"Jenkins! We have some very disturbing photographs of you at what appears to be some sort of airport homosexual orgy!"

February 20, 1987

Mrs Edwina Currie said that Glenys Kinnock was the power behind the Labour throne.

"Will it be all right if I take this apron off, Glenys, I think there's someone at the door?"

February 25, 1987

On the day that the London Daily News appeared, Lord Rothermere re-launched the Evening News as a stablemate for the Standard.

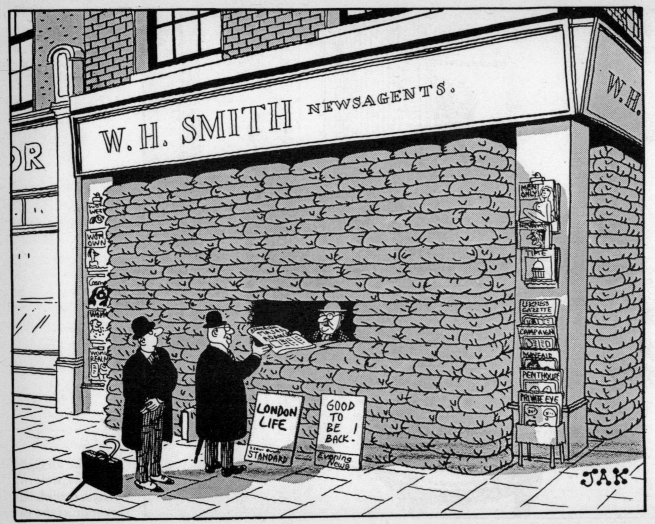

"Don't you know there a war on?"

February 27, 1987

Some ex-Nazis were said to be living in Britain, allowed to remain after the War because of their scientific knowledge.

"And here, Albert Snodgrass, alias Obergruppenfuhrer Heinrich von Muller, is someone you haven't seen or heard from in 42 years . . ."

The hunt for forme•
Nazis continued . .

"Have you ever noticed how old Walter's the only one to drink litres of Holsten lager around these parts?"

March 2, 1987

Gorbachev put forward new proposals for removing medium-range nuclear missiles from Europe.

"We won't be able to keep on meeting like this if they give up Cruise!"

March 3, 1987

A "rent boy" alleged that he'd had sessions with Russell Harty, who denied it. After inquiries, the matter was not pursued by the police.

"Dad! – It's the rent boy!"

March 4, 1987

Education Minister Kenneth Baker said that a pay deal for teachers would be enforced.

"Now, sir, do you recognise the man who forced a £600 pay rise on you in the school corridor?"

March 5, 1987

The Queen's Press Secretary resigned.

"Philip's dealing with the Press now Michael Shea's gone!"

The new Highway Code warns against using a hand-held phone while driving.

"It's for you!"

March 8, 1987

The Star newspaper saved a Spanish don[key] called Blackie by buy[ing] him and handing hi[m] over to the Internati[onal] Donkey Sanctuary Trust. But for this h[e] would have been rit[...] ridden to death at a fiesta.

"One Donkey Espagnol en Croute, Two Budgerigar Chinoise Flambe!"

March 9, 1987

President Reagan made a speech about the Iran-Contras affair, saying some of his staff were at fault; he appeared to emerge unscathed.

March 11, 1987

An ordeal for the weaker-willed . . .

March 17, 1987

Latest figures showed an all-round increase in the crime rate

"It's so bad round here sir, even the muggers have to walk around in fours!"

March 18, 1987

The basic rate of income tax was reduced in the Budget from 29p to 27p.

"Take it easy, Dolores, it only went down 2p in the pound!"

March 19, 1987

A woman doctor was struck off for being abusive to patients and staff and failing to give adequate medical attention.

"That lady doctor's cured my bloody deafness and my effing stammer!"

March 20, 1987

At a charity event, David Steel was photographed after falling on top of a lady who was wearing a low-cut dress.

"Don't forget our 50/50 deal, David!"

Retired champion
jockey Lester Piggott
was said to owe the
Inland Revenue
millions.

"Isn't that Lester Piggott on his way to the Inland Revenue?"

March 23, 1987

Seeking international recognition, Mr Kinnock went to the USA to meet President Reagan.

"I hear we've a lot in common, Mr 'er, Kinnock, my wife runs this place too!"

March 24, 1987

A captain in the Life Guards was accused in Sweden of smuggling cannabis.

"Do I know my drums are leaking cannabis? No, but if you hum it, I'll play it!"

March 26, 1987

Joan Collins did not take kindly
to a BA suggestion that she
should travel club class . . .

March 27, 1987

Cocaine addiction was said to be rife in the City.

"Do you remember him? He was always complaining about our smoking in the old office!"

Mrs Thatcher was getting on
famously with Mr Gorbachev
(Mr Kinnock, on the other
hand, had only a 20-minute chat
with President Reagan).

April 1, 1987

The Roman Catholic Church announced that it would ordain two ex-Anglicans, both of them married.

"I wish you'd stop nagging me while I'm at the office!"

April 2, 1987

A multi-million scheme to re-develop the Royal Docks was under way.

"Yes, it's a shame about breaking up the community, but the £750,000 will help!"

April 3, 1987

The Duchess of Windsor's jewels were auctioned in Geneva and fetched huge prices.

"All right, I give up, darling – what did you spend my money on today!"

April 6, 1987

Some U.S. Marines on duty in the American Embassy in Moscow were accused of spying for the Russians.

"It seems more in keeping with their current image!"

April 7, 1987

Ingenious thieves got away with a small painting by hooking it out of the window with a fishing rod.

April 9, 1987

The United States and Britain voiced threats of a trade war on Japan if that country didn't open up its markets more extensively.

"We'd like something NOT made in Japan!"

The Americans alle
that their new emba
in Moscow was full
electronic surveilla
devices planted by
Russians.

"It's for you!'

April 10, 1987

Keith Best, Tory MP for Ynys Mon, admitted making multiple applications for British Telecom shares and said he would not be standing at the General Election.

"Hello, Keith, still on the fiddle?"

April 15, 1987

Extradition procedures for Liverpool soccer fans wanted in Belgium in connection with the Heysel stadium riot, were bungled by the DPP office and the judge had to release those concerned. It was agreed later that 26 Liverpool supporters should go to Brussels to face trial.

"We don't cock 'em all up, old boy. Surely you remember how we got back Dr Crippen in 1910!"

April 21, 1987

Allegations that the late Maurice Oldfield, head of MI6, was homosexual were confirmed by Mrs Thatcher.

"I say, Carruthers! Did you pay your rent last week!"

April 23, 1987

It was forecast that there would soon be many directors earning £1 million a year.

"You can see who hasn't made it to the million-a-year bracket yet!"

April 27, 1987

A proposal was put forward that, to ease prison congestion, some prisoners might be allowed to stay at home but be equipped with an electronic tag to keep track of their movements.

"I say, Charles! Is that a new Rolex, or an electronic wrist-tag?"

April 29, 1987

Peter Wright's book Spycatcher alleged that MI5 planned the overthrow of the Wilson government.

"Have we got Ramsey MacDonald yet?"

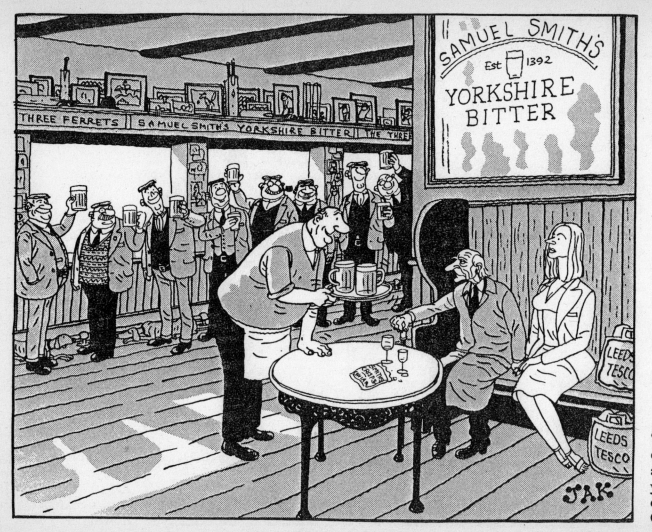

Sir Rudolph Bing, 85-year-old impresario, whose funds in the USA were frozen because he was said to be incapable of managing his financial affairs, arrived in Britian with his much younger wife.

"With the manager's compliments, Mr Bing, and if you could see your way to a couple of choruses of White Christmas . . .?"

May 1, 1987

The Standard was among newspapers that published extracts from Spycatcher, making them liable to prosecution.

"Dateline, London: As I type my last uncensored despatch, forces of the Attorney General are moving in . . .!"

Jak's advice to stately home owners plagued by young vandals.

"If the little wretch is not claimed by closing time, leave him in the Wildlife Safari Park!"

May 8, 1987

Mrs Thatcher said there had been an internal MI5 inquiry into the Spycatcher allegations about the Wilson government and there had been no such plot . . .

"Well, if there wasn't a plot, there damn well should have been!"

May 10, 1987

Former champion jockey Piggott – in trouble with the Inland Revenue and sacked Guinness chief Saunders both had their problems.

"All right then, who would you rather be – Lester Piggott or Ernest Saunders?"

May 11, 1987

The day after the London Marathon . . .

"Nice try, Gerald – no where did you really spend the night!"

May 13, 1987

Mrs Thatcher, en route for a third term in office . . .

JAK

"May I remind the Prime Minister of her promise to only remain in office until the year 2000!"

May 15, 1987

Joan Collins, who had that disagreement with BA, said they were friends again – she flew in Concorde and also bought some BA shares.

"I think British Airways are going over the top, making it up with Joan Collins!"

June 4, 1987

"Arthur George Carrick," who had a very small landscape in the Royal Academy summer exhibition, turned out to be the Prince of Wales.

"Could I have a word with you, Simpson?"

June 5, 1987

Which? magazine said some pub wine was rubbish.

"I never touch the house plonk here, but the dish-washer is full bodied with, a distinctive nose!"

June 7, 1987

President Reagan had his bed sent out for the top nations' economic summit in Venice – why shouldn't Mrs Thatcher follow suit?

"Where does Mrs Thatcher want her bed?"

June 10, 1987

Denis Healey objected to Anne Diamond bringing up the subject of Mrs Healey's hip operation, not done on the NHS.

"First, I can't watch late-night telly – now I can't watch breakfast telly!"

June 12, 1987

A sad morning after for some ex-MP's.

"I was a victim of tactical voting – I didn't get one!"

June 14,
1987

Mrs Thatcher,
enthroned again . . .

"You'll find Mrs Thatcher has taken it in her stride, Ma'am!"

June 16, 1987

The start of a disagreement between David Owen and David Steel on the question of a merger between Liberal and SDP.

"Well, speaking as a doctor, I don't think you're fit enough to be a leader!"

June 17, 1987

Many a hopeful Tory was waiting by the phone . . .

"If you're still waiting for a call from Mrs Thatcher, they're down to sub-junior Ministers for overseas drains and sewers!"

June 18, 1987

Bernard Goetz, the Subway Vigilante, was found not guilty of attempted murder.

"You ask him for his ticket, Leroy, you're wearing the bullet-proof waistcoat!"

June 19, 1987

An Iranian official was arrested on shoplifting charges and this began a round of tit-for-tat expulsions.

"We couldn't find another Englishman to send home . . . Would an Irishman do?"

June 21,
1987

The Church express
its disapproval of
Freemasons' rituals.

"An inspiring sermon, vicar – see you later at the Lodge!"

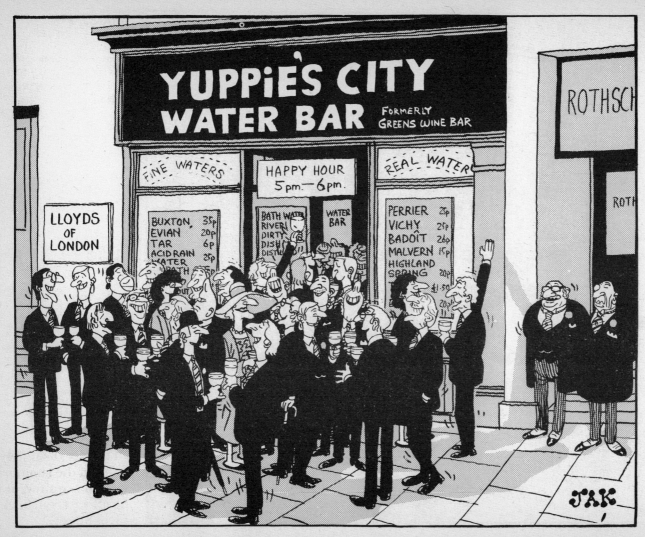

June 24, 1987

The upwardly mobile set were warned they were drinking too much at lunchtime.

"It doesn't half get them back from lunch early!"

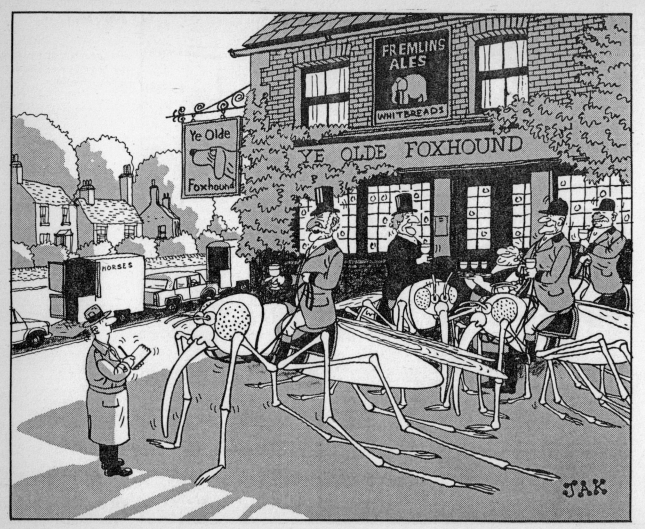

June 25, 1987

Swarms of large mosquitos, with correspondingly fierce bites, were plaguing parts of Britain.

"There is absolutely no truth in the rumours of giant mosquitos, now be off with you back to Fleet Street!"

June 26, 1987

Proposed legislation for the New Parliament included 12-hour opening for pubs.

"Right! Now how do we fill in the next twelve hours?"

June 28, 1987

Despite parents' protests a disturbing high number of children in the Cleveland area were said by doctors have been sexually abused.

JAK

"Run for it, kids – it's the hospital doctor!"

June 29, 1987

The No.1 seeded player, Boris Becker, was beaten in the first round at Wimbledon by the virtually unknown Australian, Peter Doohan.

"Germany's three days of official mourning ends today as Boris Becker is sentenced to one year in the Army!"

July 1, 1987

That's life.

"Lucky for that polecat that Esther didn't bite back!"

July 2, 1987

Rupert Murdoch added Today to his newspaper holdings

"Look! Isn't that something Rupert Murdoch hasn't bought?"

July 3, 1987

Sir Kenneth Newman, then head of the Metropolitan Police, said there was a lot of jury nobbling going on . . .

"Sorry! Was I supposed to find you not guilty for that £50,000?"

August 5, 1987

Picking an away-from-it-all holiday isn't as simple as it used to be.

"Have you got somewhere without any Moslem Fundamentalists?"

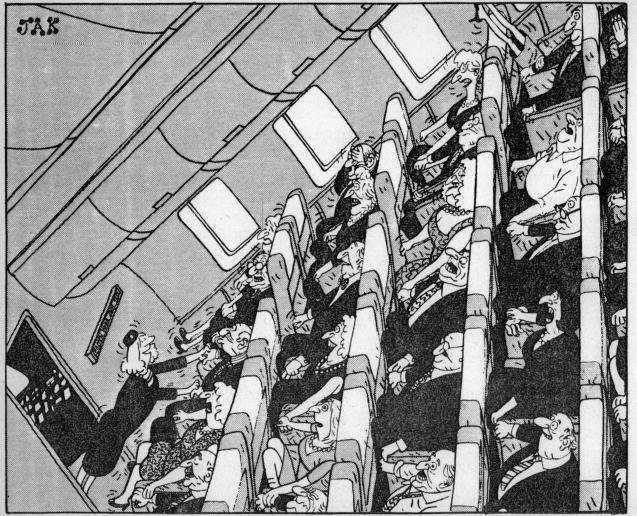

August 6, 1987

Doubts were shed on the ability of Romanian pilots flying for British Airlines.

"Is there a Rumanian speaking flying instructor on board?"

August 9, 1987

Kuwaiti tankers were being re-flagged so that they could be protected by American ships as they sailed through the Gulf.

"No, we're still under American control – but it doesn't half confuse the Iranians!"

August 11, 1987

Some bank staff worked to rule in pursuit of a pay claim.

"They're on strike, boss! – Shall we try Barclays?"

August 16, 1987

Well, they're both at home at Wembley . . .

"Personally, I think they pay these footballers far too much!"

August 18, 1987

Madonna's series of Wembley concerts over-excited many of her fans.

"Could the club secretary have a word with you, m'lud?"

August 23, 1987

An increase in Bank Rate bought panic on the Stock Exchange and wiped billions of pounds off shares.

"Henry won't leave his carphone since those billions were lost on shares last week!"

August 24, 1987

A 24-hour strike by Spanish air traffic controllers meant a frustrating time for holiday-makers.

". . . Mind you, Doris thought the beach was a bit too far!"

August 26, 1987

The King of Spain apparently made some derogatory remarks about Britons on package tours to Majorca, but it was later explained that he was misunderstood . . .

"So I said to this geezer, who do you think you are, the bleedin' King of Spain?"

August 30, 1987

The Spanish air traffic controllers' strike was causing havoc . . .

"You have it guaranteed for two weeks every year. Just think of the money you save!"

September 4, 1987

Young Mathias Rust, who landed his light plane in Red Square, was on trial in Moscow.

"Since then we have strengthened Moscow's air defences by bringing in Spanish air controllers!"

September 8, 1987

Belgians in a Brussels prison complained that Liverpool supporters awaiting trial in connection with the Heysel Stadium riot were receiving favoured treatment.

"It's not bad, mum, mind you it is a bit noisy with the Belgian prisoners complaining!"